Tales from Acorn Wood

MAKE AND DO BOOK

Based on the books by

JULIA DONALDSON ❧ AXEL SCHEFFLER

MACMILLAN CHILDREN'S BOOKS

Hints and Tips to Read With a Grown-Up

Are you ready to get creative? There are lots of fun ideas in this book for brilliant things to make and do. Before you get started, read through these hints and tips with a grown-up.

- Have a grown-up with you at all times when doing any of the activities in this book, and make sure you ask for help if you find any of the steps a bit tricky.

- Be very careful when using scissors, and always check with a grown-up first to make sure they're not too sharp and are safe for you to use.

- Before you start an activity, read the instructions together so you can make sure you have everything you need.

- Some of these craft ideas can get messy, so wear an apron or old clothes that your grown-up doesn't mind you getting dirty. It's a good idea to tie your hair back if it's long to stop it getting in the way.

- It's best to work on a wipe-clean surface, but you could always cover the floor and table with used newspapers or an old cloth, too.

- Remember to wash your hands after using paint, glue or anything else that might make a mess.

- Arts and crafts can be a great way to reuse things that you might otherwise throw away. For example, you could cut up an old cereal box instead of buying new card. On the next page, you can see a list of some things you might need for the activities in this book. Why not ask your friends and family to help you start saving them?

Things to collect:

Brown paper grocery bags
A takeaway coffee cup with a lid
Toilet roll tubes
String and wool
Old clean socks

Paper plates and cups
A used juice carton
Old garden pegs
Wooden spoons
Lolly sticks

How to use your templates:

You can find some drawings on the back of your sticker pages that you can use to make templates that will help you with some of the activities in this book, like the feathers for Rock and Roll Hen on pages 12 and 13. Here's how to make your templates:

1 Lay a piece of thin paper or tracing paper over the outline on the back of your sticker page. Draw over it with a pencil.

2 Carefully cut out your drawing and glue it to a piece of card.

3 Now cut around your drawing so that you have a piece of card the same shape as the original outline. This is your template! You can draw around it as many times as you like.

How to use your stickers:

There are two pages of stickers at the end of this book. They have been specially designed for you to decorate the things you make, but you might prefer to draw your own decorations.

Now you're all set to start – so roll up your sleeves, get out your pens and pencils and have fun!

Finger-Hop Rabbit

Try making fingerprint pictures of Rabbit.
Why not print a field of crunchy finger carrots, too?

Hopping Rabbit

You will need:

Light brown paint
A saucer for the paint
An A4 sheet of plain paper
A black pen

What to do:

1 Pour a small amount of paint into the saucer.

2 Let's make the face first. Dip your 'pointing' finger into the paint then press it on to the paper. For the body, make another fingerprint below.

3 Wash your hands and wait for the paint to dry.

4 On the top fingerprint, draw eyes or add stickers from your sticker sheet. Draw in a mouth, nose and long twitchy whiskers.

5 On the bottom fingerprint, draw arms and legs. Now all Rabbit needs is a fluffy tail. Draw it in.

6 Experiment with different fingers to make lots of fingerprint tops and bottoms of Rabbit.

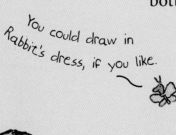

You could draw in Rabbit's dress, if you like.

Crunchy Finger Carrots

You could use an old brown paper bag instead of craft paper.

You will need:

Safety scissors
A small sheet of craft
  paper (about half-A4 size)
Glue
An A4 sheet of white
  paper
Orange paint
A saucer for the paint
A green pencil or pen

What to do:

1 Cut the craft paper to cover the bottom half of the sheet of white paper and stick it down.

2 Pour a small amount of paint into the saucer.

3 To make carrots, dip a finger into the paint. Start at the top of the brown paper and make three prints going downwards, each one getting a little bit smaller.

4 Wash your hands. Wait for the paint to dry.

5 Now all you need to do is scribble little green leaves on the top of each carrot, as if just poking above the ground.

Tips, Tricks and Twists

 If you don't have craft paper, you could paint the soil with brown paint.

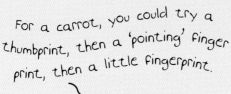

For a carrot, you could try a thumbprint, then a 'pointing' finger print, then a little fingerprint.

Bear's Birthday Cake

Bear is in the kitchen. Watch him cook.
Hip, hip, hooray! Let's make a brilliant birthday cake.

You will need:

Seven paper cups
A small piece of sponge
Paints
Two A4 sheets of paper
Glue that dries clear
A hole punch
Safety scissors
Stiff red card (about
   half-A4 size)
Sticky tape

What to do:

1 It's time for some messy dip and dab sponge painting! First, turn the cups upside down.

2 Now dip the sponge into brown paint and dab each cup again and again. Then dip the sponge into yellow paint and do the same. Dip and dab until the cups are completely covered in paint. Wait for them to dry.

3 Arrange the cups in a circle. Dab glue around each rim and stick on to a sheet of paper.

4 To make paper sprinkles, use the hole punch to make lots of holes in a sheet of paper. Ask a grown-up to empty the hole punch and find your sprinkles inside.

5 Dab glue on the tops and sides of your cups. Then gently throw the sprinkles over the cups. Scoop up any that don't stick and throw and sprinkle again.

6   To make the candles, cut seven thick strips of the red card. Dip each one in yellow paint and wait for them to dry.

7   Fold the bottom of each candle back and then tape the fold of each candle to a cup.

Tips, Tricks and Twists

   If you don't have a hole punch, you could snip up tiny scraps of coloured paper to make rainbow sprinkles.

   Why don't you decorate the sheet of paper to look like a table cloth? You could use your stickers or add your own drawings.

How old are you? You could put the same number of candles on your cake.

Fox's Stripy Bow Tie

In a cupboard up high,
He finds his bow tie.
Make and wear your very own stripy bow tie and look as splendid as Fox.

You will need:

A pencil
A small piece of white card
  (about half-A4 size)
Safety scissors
Black and green pens
A small bulldog clip
Strong sticky tape

What to do:

1 First draw the shape of the bow tie on to the card. You can use the template at the back of your sticker sheet to help. Cut it out.

2 Decide which side is the front. Using your pens, draw black lines to show the knot in the middle of the bow. Then add in lots of green stripes.

3 Lay the bulldog clip on the back of the bow tie, in the middle. Use strong sticky tape to secure one arm of the bulldog clip to the bow tie.

4 Now you're ready to wear your bow tie by clipping the bulldog clip to the top of your shirt or T-shirt.

How about wearing a snazzy bow tie as a brooch or on a hat?

Tips, Tricks and Twists

🐝 You could decorate your bow tie in all sorts of ways. Use paint, colouring pencils or stick on cut-out paper to make it lovely and colourful. Or you could add stickers from your sticker sheet.

🐝 Why not make a bow tie with a special pattern and give it to a friend as a surprise present?

Deep in Acorn Wood

In this special picture of an oak tree, the shape of your hand makes the branches and your fingerprints the acorns.

You will need:

An A4 sheet of craft paper
A pencil
Safety scissors
An A4 sheet of blue paper
Glue
Brown and green paint
Two saucers for the paint
A sheet of green paper
  (about half-A4 size)

What to do:

1 Place the sheet of craft paper with the short sides at the top and bottom.

2 Draw around your hand, from the top of your wrist all the way around your fingers back to the other side of your wrist.

3 Cut out your hand shape, taking care around the shape of your fingers.

4 Place the blue sheet of paper with the short sides at the top and bottom. Stick your brown hand shape on to the blue paper. This is your tree.

5 For the acorns, pour each colour of paint into a saucer.

6 First dip a finger into the brown paint. Then press it down near the edge of the tree shape. Do this again and again to make brown fingerprints along the branches. Wash your hands and wait for the paint to dry.

7 Now dip your little finger into the green paint. Print on top of one of your brown fingerprints. Dip and print again and again to make all the pretty acorn cups. Let the paint dry.

8 Your tree is nearly fully grown. Just cut small leaf shapes from the green paper and stick a leaf to the bottom of each acorn.

You could use an old brown paper bag instead of craft paper.

Tips, Tricks and Twists

- You could try drawing the acorns instead of printing them, or you could cut out acorn shapes from old magazines and stick them on to your tree.

- Why not add stickers of the Acorn Wood animals and lots of acorns from your sticker sheet?

Rock and Roll Hen

Whee! This paper-plate toy Hen rolls and pecks.

See page 3 to find out how to make your templates.

You will need:

A pencil
Small sheets of red, brown
   and yellow card (each
   about half-A4 size)
Safety scissors
A white paper plate
Paintbrushes
Paints
Sticky tape

What to do:

1 On the red card, draw the outline of the big feathers on top of Hen's head and cut them out. You can use the templates on the back of your sticker sheet to help.

2 Cut out a triangle of yellow card for the beak and fold it in half.

3 Paint the middle circle of your paper plate to look like Hen's blue and white spotty dress.

4 Fold the paper plate in half and gently press down along the fold.

5 Stick Hen's big red feathers to the plate near the fold line. You can copy the picture on the opposite page.

6 Carefully slide the beak inside the folded plate so it's poking out, then stick in place with tape.

7 Hen needs eyes! Paint one on either side, or use stickers from your sticker sheet.

8 Stand the folded plate up so the folded edge is at the top and gently push Hen to make her rock.

Why not make a paper-plate yellow chick?

Tips, Tricks and Twists

 Try making the top big feathers look like real feathers – gently roll the paper around a pencil to make them curl.

 You could decorate Hen with cut-out paper collage feathers, or paint some on.

Who Can It Be?

Make your own mask and pretend to be Bear.

You will need:

A brown paper bag,
  as big as your face
Brown craft paper
Glue
A pencil
Safety scissors
Paintbrushes
White and black paint
A hole punch
A length of elastic
  to go around
  your head

What to do:

Make the holes on either side of the mask with a hole punch, if you have one.

1 Place the bag on the table, with the open edge at the bottom. Open the bag slightly and spread glue inside. Press gently to stick the layers together and let the glue dry.

2 Hold the bag to your face and ask a grown-up to mark with the pencil where the eye holes should go.

3 Ask your grown-up to cut out the eye holes.

4 Paint a white circle all the way around each eye hole. Then paint thinner black lines around the eye holes and white circles.

5 Bear needs a nose and a mouth! Paint a nose, then a downwards line and a smiley mouth. You can copy the picture.

6 For the ears, cut two half-circles from brown paper. Paint a black line around the top and paint the insides white.

7   Glue the ears to the top of the mask. Wait for the glue to dry.

8   Ask your grown-up to make a hole on each side of the mask, level with the eye holes, using the hole punch or scissors.

9   Are you ready to wear your mask? Ask your grown-up to cut a length of elastic to fit around the back of your head, plus extra for tying. Thread one end of the elastic through a hole in the mask and tie in a knot, then thread the other end through the second hole and tie to secure. Now pop your mask on and pretend to be Bear!

When you put on your mask, you will look just like Bear.

Tips, Tricks and Twists

- If you don't have a brown paper bag, you could use brown craft paper. Or you could paint a sheet of white paper brown.

- Try decorating your mask with coloured paints and pencils to look like Bear's soft fur. You could stick on paper shapes, too.

Fox's Sock Puppet

Poor old Fox
Has lost his socks.
Find an old sock and use it to make a fun puppet.

You will need:

An old clean sock
A felt tip pen
A small plastic bag
Strong glue
A paintbrush
Red paint
Safety scissors
Coloured wool
  (1 metre length)

What to do:

1 First put the sock on your hand with the heel on your knuckles. The part covering your fingers will be the puppet's face.

2 Ask a grown-up to mark two small dots with a felt tip pen where the eyes will go.

3 Ask your grown-up to mark where the mouth will go, too. Now it's time to take your hand out of the sock.

4 While you make the puppet, to stop the glue sticking the sock together, slip a small plastic bag inside the bottom of the sock.

What does your sock puppet sound like?
You could put on a funny voice.

5 Glue on eyes from your sticker sheet.

6 For the mouth, paint a little red semi-circle. You might need to paint two coats to make the red colour really show.

7 For the twisty mop of hair, cut your length of wool into three equal pieces.

8 Carefully hold all the lengths of wool together and tie a knot in the middle. Then tie another knot on top.

9 Glue the knot above the eyes on the top of the head. Wait for the glue to dry.

10 Are you ready? It's time to put your hand into the sock puppet. Move your fingers up and down to make it look as if the puppet is talking.

Why not make a stripy sock puppet?

Tips, Tricks and Twists

- You could cut out a bow tie or hat from coloured card to stick on, too.

- For the eyes, you could ask your grown-up to help you sew on round buttons. Or you could cut out and stick on eyes made from big circles of white felt and small circles of black felt.

Bird Feeder

Keep the birds outside happy with a feeder in the shape of Blackbird.

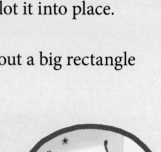

You will need:

An old juice carton, washed and dried
Scissors
Paintbrushes
Red, yellow and black waterproof paints
Two plastic bottle tops
Strong glue
A lolly stick
String
Birdseed

What to do:

1 Ask your grown-up to cut two slots near the bottom of the carton, one at the front and one at the back. They should be the same width as your lolly stick and need to line up so you can slot it into place.

2 Now ask your grown-up to cut out a big rectangle above the slot at the front.

3 To make Blackbird's wings, ask your grown-up to make two cuts in each side of the carton, like two sides of a triangle. Carefully lift up each wing so they look like they're flapping.

Tips, Tricks and Twists

 Your grown-up could use a craft knife to cut out the shapes. If they use scissors, it's best to pierce the card with the sharp end of the scissors, then make small cuts.

 Can you think of any other way you could decorate your bird feeder? Maybe you could use the Peg Painting techniques on pages 26 and 27.

4 Now paint the carton to look just like Blackbird. At the bottom, paint red for his jumper and paint the rest of the carton black. Don't forget to paint a yellow triangle for his beak!

5 Lay the two bottle tops down so the insides are facing up. Paint them white. Once dry, add a small black dot in the middle of each one. These are Blackbird's eyes! Glue them on to the carton above his beak.

6 To make a perch for real birds, push the lolly stick through the slots from front to back.

7 Fill your carton with birdseed, then tie string securely around the cap at the top so that you can hang up your bird feeder outside.

Postman Bear's Invitation

Bear is writing letters.
One, two, three.
It's party time! Ask a friend to tea with an
invitation in the shape of Postman Bear.

Take your time and draw as carefully as you can.

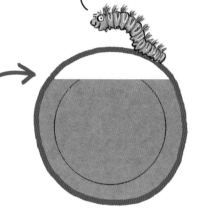

You will need:

An A4 sheet of brown
   craft paper
A small tin, such as
   a tin of beans
Safety scissors
A small sheet of cream
   paper
Glue
A black pen

What to do:

1 Fold the sheet of craft paper
   in half. Place the tin on top so
   that it just overlaps the folded
   edge and draw around it, then
   remove the tin.

2 You should have a shape that looks like a circle with
   a small piece missing. This is Bear's face! Cut it out
   to make your card.

3 For Bear's ears, draw two small circles on your
   leftover craft paper and cut them out.

4 Draw two slightly smaller
   circles on the cream paper
   and cut them out. Stick them
   in the middle of the craft
   paper circles.

5 Glue the ears at the top of the
   card, poking up behind the fold.

6 Draw another circle on the cream paper and cut it out, then stick it in the middle of Bear's face.

7 Draw Bear's nose and mouth on the cream circle. Don't forget to give him a smile! Then add his eyes – you could draw them or use your stickers.

Tips, Tricks and Twists

 Try making more party invitations. You could change the colour of the paper and the shape of the ears and make Rabbit or Fox!

 If you want to make a bigger card, draw around a bigger object like a bowl.

What will you write inside? Decorate your message with stickers.

COME TO MY PARTY

Make Music with the Mice

Bash! Clash! Who's that?
Oh no! A band of mice.
Let's make noisy musical instruments to shake and drum!

Shaker

You will need:

A cardboard ice-cream
  tub with a lid
Paintbrushes
Green and blue paints
Dried beans or lentils

What to do:

1 Ask a grown-up to wash and dry your tub and lid.
   Now you can paint them! Paint three stripes of
   colour on the tub: light green for grass, dark green
   for trees and blue for the sky. Paint the lid blue, too.

2 Once the paint is dry, look on your sticker
   page to find your favourite Acorn Wood
   friends and stick them to your tub.

3 Pop a spoonful or two of dried lentils
   into the cup and put on the lid.

4 Shake your shaker to make
   lots of noise!

Which animals will
you choose?

Spinning Drum

With your thumb on the top of the handle, turn your wrist and drum.

You will need:

Two small paper plates
Paintbrushes
Paints
Safety scissors
String
Two small beads
Sticky tape
Two lolly sticks
Strong glue

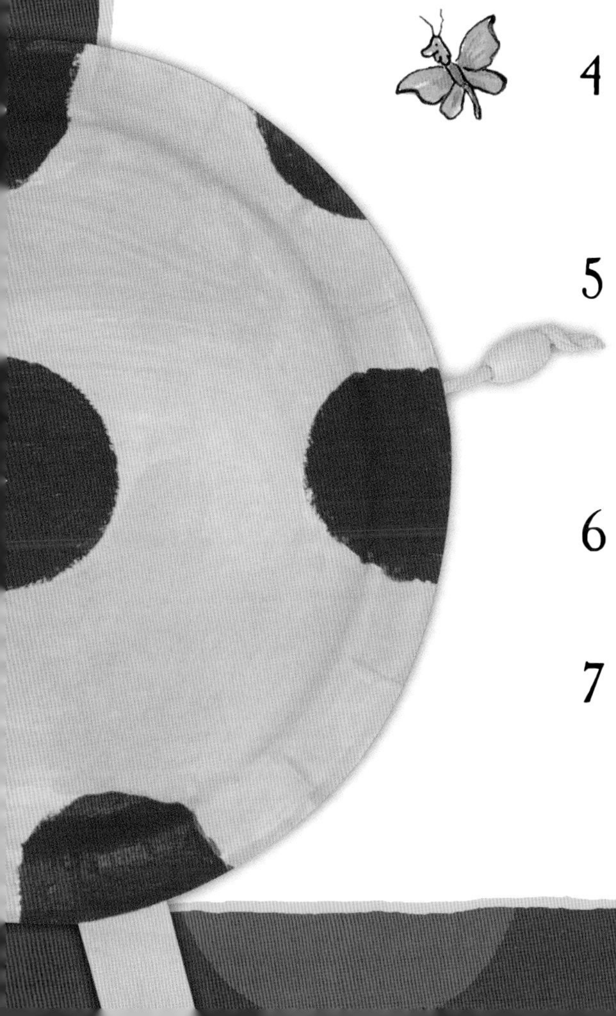

What to do:

1 Lay your plates upside down and paint them. You can do any pattern you like – how about spots or stripes? Leave to dry.

2 Ask your grown-up to cut a 30cm length of string. Thread a bead on to each end and secure each one with a double knot.

3 Place one plate in front of you with the painted side facing down. Lay the string across the middle, with an equal length off the plate on each side. Tape it securely to the plate, in the middle and at the edges.

4 Now tape a lolly stick to the inside of the plate at the bottom, so most of it is poking out. Tape the other lolly stick to the inside of the other plate.

5 Spread glue around the inside edge of the plate that has the string taped to it. Quickly stick the other plate on top so that the painted side faces up and the lolly sticks line up.

6 Press down the edges to make the glue stick, then wait for it to dry.

7 Wrap sticky tape around both lolly sticks to make a nice, strong handle. Now you are ready to drum!

Play Acorn Catch

This paper cup game is fun to play on your own
or with your friends!

Use your templates to draw
the animals' ears.

You will need:

Four paper cups
Paintbrushes
Paints
Safety scissors
Coloured card: dark brown,
   light brown, pink, white
   and orange
Glue
A pink button
A black felt tip pen
A small sheet of green paper

Fox

1 Paint a cup orange and let it dry.

2 Cut out two ovals from white card and glue them
on the sides of the cup, leaving a space for the
nose in the middle.

3 Cut out two triangular ears from the orange card.
Stick them on to the top of the cup at the back.

4 Add stickers for eyes from your sticker sheet.
At the bottom of the cup, draw on a big black
nose and long whiskers.

Rabbit

1 Paint a cup light brown and let it dry.

2 Cut out two long ears from light brown
card. Stick them on to the top of the
cup at the back.

3 Add stickers for eyes from your sticker
sheet, then draw a nose, mouth
and whiskers.

If you don't have coloured card,
just use white card and paint
it the right colour.

Pig

1 Paint a cup pink and let it dry.

2 Cut out two small pointy ears from pink card. Stick them on to the top of the cup at the back.

3 Add stickers for eyes from your sticker sheet. Glue on a button for the nose, then draw Pig's smile underneath.

Bear

1 Paint a cup dark brown and let it dry.

2 Cut out two round ears from dark brown card. Stick them on to the top of the cup at the back.

3 Add stickers for eyes from your sticker sheet, then draw on Bear's nose and smiling mouth.

How to play

Scrunch up five pieces of green paper to make acorns. Pop the cups in a row on a table, stand back and take it in turns to see who can throw an acorn into a cup. You could give a point for each one you get in! Why not move one further away to make it more difficult? You could give extra points for that.

Peg Painting in the Woods

Whoosh! Dab! Splat!
Paint with homemade peg paintbrushes.

You will need:

Six pegs
Six things to make the tips
   of the brushes, including a
   small leaf, a twig, a flower,
   a ball of string, a small
   piece of sponge and a
   feather
Six different coloured paints,
   each in a saucer
A sheet of A4 plain paper

What to do:

1 First make your peg paintbrushes. Hold a peg open and put a leaf, feather or anything else you like in the open end, then close it. Mind your fingers!

2 It's best to get everything ready before you paint. Lay out your peg paintbrushes and the saucers of different coloured paint.

3 First dip the end of one peg paintbrush into some paint, then on to the sheet of paper. What kind of shapes and patterns does it make?

4 Now try a different peg paintbrush with a different coloured paint. Experiment making all kinds of whoosh, dab and splat marks with your paintbrushes.

Have fun and make lots of bright, colourful painty pictures.

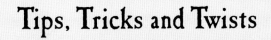

Come up with your own things for the ends of your peg paintbrushes, too. Go wild!

Tips, Tricks and Twists

🌰 You could use a peg paintbrush to mix together different paints on your paper and make some really amazing colourful swirls.

🌰 Try painting a picture of Acorn Wood. When it's dry, you could draw on your favourite animals or use your stickers.

🌰 Create a frame by making marks with a peg paintbrush again and again, all the way around the edge of a sheet of paper.

Put on a Puppet Show

Create your very own wooden spoon puppets
and put on an Acorn Wood show.

Look on the back of your sticker pages to find templates to help you.

You will need:

Four wooden spoons
Paintbrushes
Paints
Safety scissors
Small pieces of orange,
  pink, white, cream, dark
  and light brown paper
Glue
A black felt tip pen
A scrap of black felt
A pink button
String
A short length of green wool

Rabbit

1 Paint the round part of a spoon light brown, then paint the handle green with white spots, just like Rabbit's dress. Wait for the paint to dry.

2 Cut out two long ears from light brown paper. Stick them to the back of the spoon so they poke up.

3 To make whiskers, cut two 15cm lengths of string. Tie them together with a knot in the middle, then glue the knot in the middle of Rabbit's face.

4 Draw on a mouth with a felt tip pen.

5 Add eyes from your sticker sheet.

Instead of using coloured paper for the ears you could paint plain paper different colours.

Bear

1 Paint the round part of a spoon dark brown, then paint the handle red for Bear's smart waistcoat. Leave to dry.

2 Cut out two round ears from dark brown paper. Stick them to the back of the spoon so they poke up.

3 Draw a small circle on your cream paper, then cut it out. Stick it on the round part of the spoon.

4 Draw Bear's nose and smiling mouth on the cream circle.

5 Add eyes from your sticker sheet.

Pig

1 Paint the round part of a spoon pink, then paint the handle yellow with red flowers to look like Pig's dress.

2 Cut out two pointy ears from pink paper. Stick them to the back of the spoon so they poke up.

3 When the paint is dry, glue on a pink button for a nose and draw on a smile.

4 Add eyes from your sticker sheet.

Fox

1 Paint the round part of a spoon orange, then paint the handle pale blue for Fox's shirt. Wait for the paint to dry.

2 Cut out two pointy ears from the orange paper. Stick them to the back of the spoon so they poke up.

3 Draw two small ovals on your cream paper and cut them out. Stick them on to the round part of the spoon – you can copy the picture below.

4 For the whiskers, cut three lengths of string about 10 cm long. Stick the middle of each length to the round part of the spoon, near where it joins the handle.

5 For the nose, cut out a small round circle of black felt and stick it on the middle of the string whiskers.

6 Add eyes from your sticker sheet.

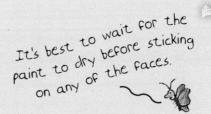

It's best to wait for the paint to dry before sticking on any of the faces.

You will need:

Three toilet roll tubes
Paintbrushes
Paints
Safety scissors
A craft knife
A piece of card (about
　half-A4 size)
Glue
Blue paper (about
　half-A4 size)
An A4 sheet of thin
　green card
A pencil
Blue and green paper

Frog's Pond House

1 Paint a toilet roll tube brown.

2 To make the roof, cut a piece of card about
5cm x 5cm and fold it in half. Paint it brown,
then wait for the paint to dry.

3 To make the jetty, cut a strip of card about 4cm
x 10cm and paint it brown. When dry, make a
fold about 2cm from the end. Cut away a square
to make legs.

4 About halfway up the tube, ask a grown-up to
cut out a three-sided door using a craft knife or
sharp scissors. Carefully fold open the door.

5 Ask your grown-up to cut a slit beneath the
door the same width as the jetty. Now you can
slot the jetty into place!

6 Pop the roof on top. You could add a few dabs
of glue to keep it in place.

7 All the house needs now is a pond. Cut out a
big puddle shape from blue paper, and sit Frog's
house on top of it.

Mole's House

1 Cut a tube in half and paint it brown. When dry, draw on a door. Don't forget the door knob!

2 Ask a grown-up to cut out two sides of the door, then fold it open.

3 Ask a grown-up to cut a long strip of green card. Pop your painted tube near one end of the strip, then make a fold just after it. Bend the card over the tube to make a grassy mound, then stick it down.

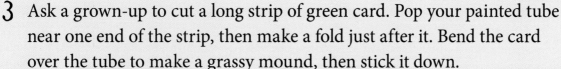

Why not decorate your houses with the stickers on your sticker page?

Squirrel's Tree

1 Paint a toilet roll tube brown and wait for it to dry.

2 At the bottom of the tube, ask a grown-up to cut out two sides of a door. Fold the door open.

3 Using the template on the back of your sticker sheet, draw a treetop shape on green card and cut it out.

4 At the top of the tube, ask your grown-up to cut a slit either side and slot in your treetop.

It's showtime!

Why not make up a story for your puppets to act out? You could make extra puppets of Mole, Squirrel or Frog – or find them on your sticker page and put them in their houses. To put on a show, pop your houses on a table and sit quietly just beneath it, out of sight. Poke your puppets above the table edge, then move them around and make them talk. Bravo!

First published 2021 by Macmillan Children's Books
an imprint of Pan Macmillan
The Smithson, 6 Briset Street, London EC1M 5NR
Associated companies throughout the world
www.panmacmillan.com

ISBN: 978-1-5290-4640-3

Based on the bestselling Tales from Acorn Wood series
by Julia Donaldson and Axel Scheffler
Text copyright © Julia Donaldson 2000, 2021
Illustrations copyright © Axel Scheffler 2000, 2021
Moral rights asserted.

1 3 5 7 9 8 6 4 2

A CIP catalogue record for this book is available from the British Library.

Printed in China

Bear's Birthday Cake

Fox's Stripy Bow Tie

Deep in Acorn Wood

Make Music with the Mice

You might find these templates helpful when making some of your crafts.
Have a look on page 3 to find out how to use them.

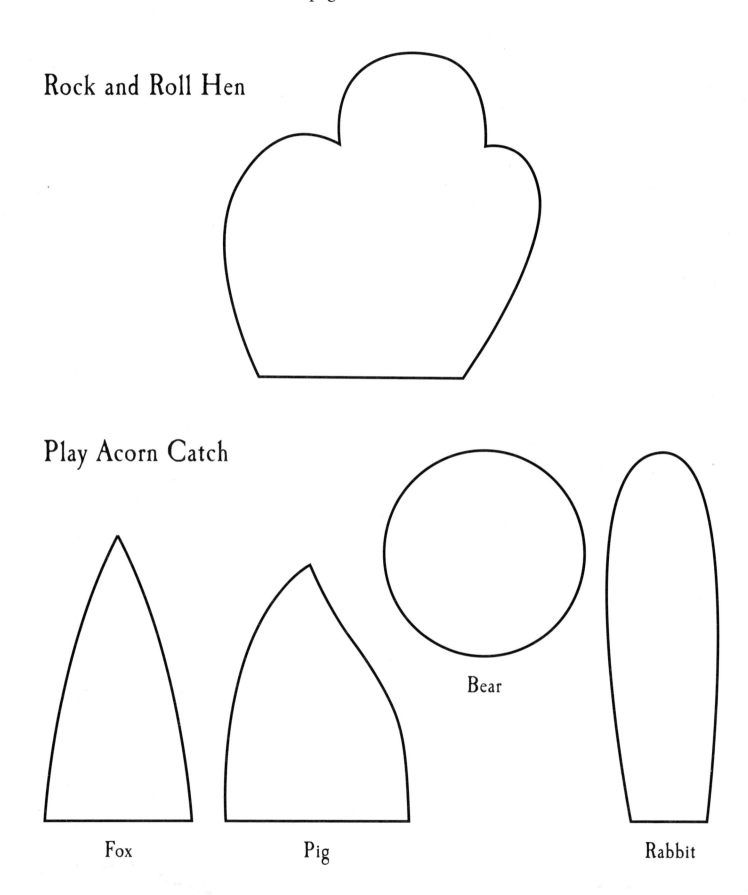

Rock and Roll Hen

Play Acorn Catch

Fox

Pig

Bear

Rabbit

Fox's Stripy Bow Tie

Squirrel's Tree House

Put on a
Puppet Show

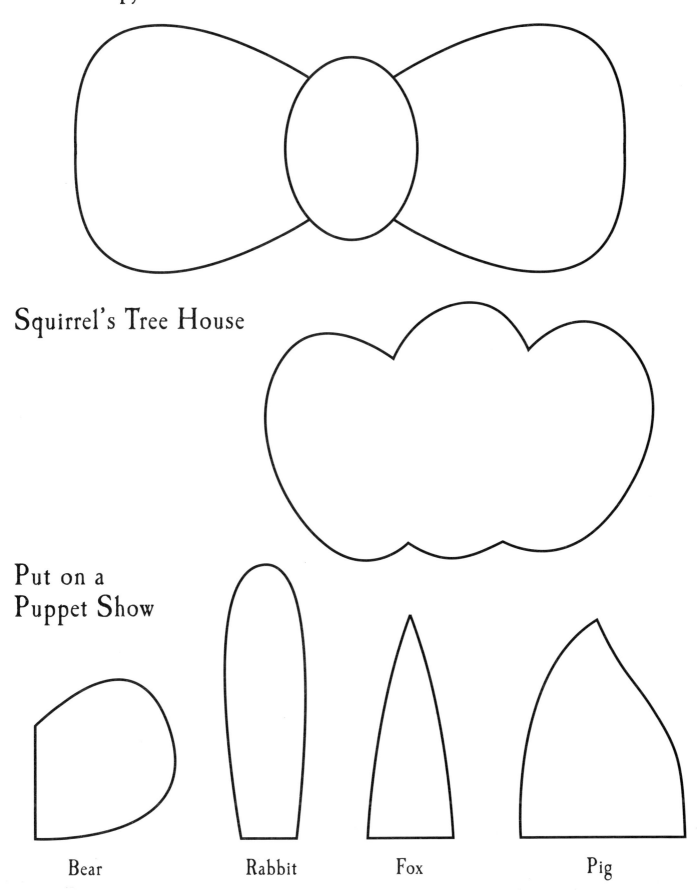

Bear   Rabbit   Fox   Pig

Peg Painting in the Woods

Put on a Puppet Show

Here are some extra stickers to decorate your crafts

These eyes will come in handy for lots of your crafts, like the Finger-hop Rabbits, Fox's Sock Puppet and more